ELI KETILSSON

99, —

# NORWAY –
# HOME OF THE TROLLS

MEDUSA

*When the sun goes down*
*and night falls,*
*the trolls take over.*
*The hulder nymphs celebrate weddings,*
*trolls pay visits to one another,*
*and the water troll screeches from the lake…*
*God help you if you venture out!*

*While the moon is up*
*anything can happen...*
*Suddenly*
*you can experience*
*the transformation of the dark forest*
*into an enormous, ugly troll –*
*lumbering straight towards you!*

High on the hillside sits the witch,
turning the spinning wheel of spite.
Her wool is mixed with
wickedness and slander,
gossip, envy and malice.
How busy she is!

*Sometimes the troll has only one eye.*
*But how that one eye*
*shines and sparkles!*
*With gold and glitter*
*– and horror and fear…*

*Deep in the forest*
*is a quiet lake,*
*bright and inviting*
*and bordered by dark firs.*
*Is that really an old,*
*gnarled tree root*
*floating there?*
*Beware!*
*It is the water troll*
*lying in wait,*
*ready to grab you*
*with his wet and slimy hands...*

*Sometimes the water troll becomes*
*a shining jewel*
*gleaming at the water's edge.*
*The moment you touch it you are in his power.*
*Or he becomes a beautiful white horse,*
*grazing and confident*
*that someone will mount his powerful back.*
*Whereupon he plunges into the water with his prey!*

*Trolls are as big and strong as fifty men,*
*but their sense*
*doesn't match their physical might.*
*They can be so stupid, clumsy and gullible*
*that even plucky little boys*
*can outwit them.*

The third time the same thing happened again. The troll lured Butterball from his hiding place with the promise of a small silver spoon, got him into the sack and rushed straight home with him. There she asked her daughter to chop him up and make a stew of him, while she herself went off to invite some guests to the feast.

But the troll's daughter did not know exactly how to go about these things.

– Wait, and I'll show you how to do it, said Butterball. – Put your head on the stool and you'll see.

The poor thing did as she was told – and Butterball chopped off her head. Then he placed her head in the bed and her body in the cauldron, while he hid above the door with the fir root and the stone.

When the trolls came home and saw the head in the bed, they thought their daughter was asleep. They decided to taste the stew.

– Mm, tastes delicious, Butterball stew! said the troll hag.

– Mm, tastes delicious, daughter stew! said Butterball. But they did not pay attention.

Then the mountain troll took his spoon and tasted the food.

– Mm, tastes delicious, Butterball stew! he said.

– Mm, tastes delicious, daughter stew! said Butterball from his hiding place above the door.

This time they began to wonder who was talking, and decided to go out and have a look. But when they reached the door, Butterball dropped the fir root and the stone on to their heads and killed them. He took all the gold and silver he could find, and you can imagine how rich he became. And then he went home to his mother.

*(Norwegian folk tale)*

Hauskvarningen hentar Snøsbuk

# BUTTERBALL

Once upon a time there was a little boy called Butterball. Butterball was his name because he was so fat and chubby and fond of good food. One day he and his mother heard somebody approaching the farm house, and she asked Butterball to go and see who it was.

– Oh, heaven help me! Here comes a big, tall troll hag with her head under her arm and a sack on her back!

– Run and hide under the kitchen table, said his mother.

The big troll came in, asked for Butterball, and said it was a pity he was not home:

– I've a fine little silver knife I wanted to give him, said the troll.

– Hey! Here I am! said Butterball from under the kitchen table.

– I'm so old and my back is so stiff. You'll have to search inside the sack and find it yourself, said the troll.

Butterball did just that. Whereupon the troll swung the sack on to her back and rushed out through the door.

But after a while the troll got tired and put down the sack to take a nap. Butterball wasted no time. He took his knife, cut a hole in the sack and slipped out. Then he put a large fir root in the sack in his place. When the troll hag came home and discovered what was in the sack, she was furious.

The next day the troll hag came visiting again, and Butterball hid under the table. This time the troll hag said she had a silver fork she wanted to give him. Butterball came out from under the table, and the troll managed to lure him into the sack again. But once again the troll became tired and went off to have a nap, and Butterball climbed out and placed a big stone in the sack in his stead.

When the troll hag came home, she emptied the sack straight into the cauldron. The stone fell out and made a large hole in the cauldron. The troll was even more furious.

*Trolls can become incredibly old,
so old that moss and trees grow on them.
When they shout to one another,
they sometimes have to wait
a hundred years for an answer.
Sometimes they grow so old
that they cannot remember
how old they really are...*

*A troll may carry his head under his arm,*
*or he can have several heads —*
*three, six, nine …*
*What a noise they make,*
*arguing and shouting*
*when all the heads try to speak at once!*
*The troll may even forget*
*to hide himself from the sun…*

*The trolls are at their wildest in winter,*
*when the sun is absent from northern skies.*
*You must never venture out alone on Christmas Eve!*
*In summer you are fairly safe,*
*for then they hardly dare*
*poke their long noses*
*outside their front doors…*
*Noses which can be put to many uses!*

TIL KJELTUSEN: INGEN HAR KALDT MIG TIL JUL

*As day breaks in the east,*
*and the pink glow of morning tints the hill,*
*the trolls must hide.*
*For, however huge and strong they may be,*
*whatever tricks they may devise,*
*these powers of darkness cannot survive*
*the sun's rays.*
*They shatter,*
*or are turned to stone.*

*Trolls are never in a rush.*
*On their journey to a feast*
*they lumber over mountains and long ridges.*
*Most often they err in circles,*
*as they never agree on*
*the right way to go...*
*Sometimes it takes them a hundred years.*

Parental Pride.

*Trolls like to throw stones,*
*especially at church spires,*
*as they hate the sound of church bells.*
*Fortunately they always miss.*
*But that is why you see*
*so many strange stones round churches.*

*All kinds of mosses and woodland plants*
*grow in the trolls' hair,*
*and birds build nests there.*
*That is why trolls especially appreciate*
*having beautiful princesses stroke their heads,*
*princesses they abduct to their mountain.*

*The trolls are inconceivably rich.*
*They live surrounded by gold and silver*
*and masses of glittering treasure.*
*Their cattle are plumper*
*and superior to any you have ever seen.*
*And they are always at constant odds*
*with human beings:*

*– Fee fi fo fum, I smell the blood of a Christian!*

*Over and over again*
*the Ash Lad has to set out*
*on long and hazardous journeys,*
*east of the sun and west of the moon.*
*He is forced to face countless dangers.*
*But far, far away he sees something*
*shining and glistening –*
*Soria Moria Castle …*

*When the princess has given to the Ash Lad
the troll's elixir of strength,
he is able to wield the heavy troll sword
as easily as a feather,
and manages to cut off all the troll's heads
at a single blow.*

*A bear, you think?*
*O no, it is the handsome prince*
*a troll hag has transformed,*
*condemning him to be a white bear by day.*

*— Have you ever ridden more comfortably,*
*ever seen more clearly? he asked.*
*— Never! she replied.*
*Thus he knew that she was the one,*
*the one who would redeem him.*

*Once upon a time there was a queen*
*who had twelve sons*
*but no daughter.*
*One day she did a deal with a troll hag:*
*she was given a daughter,*
*but her sons became wild ducks*
*and flew away…*

*In order to rescue her brothers,*
*the princess had to gather*
*enough cotton grass*
*to weave the cloth for and make twelve caps,*
*twelve shirts and twelve kerchiefs.*
*And do this without speaking,*
*laughing or weeping...*
*Only thus could the princes be redeemed.*

# THE ASH LAD'S EATING CONTEST WITH THE TROLL

Once upon a time there was a farmer who had three sons. He was a poor man, old and feeble, and his sons wouldn't turn their hands to a thing. A fine large forest belonged to the farm, and in order to pay off some of his debts, the farmer wanted the boys to chop wood there.

Eventually, the eldest son agreed to go. When he had started felling a shaggy spruce, a big, burly troll appeared.

– If you chop wood in my forest, I shall kill you! said the troll.

When the boy heard that, he threw the axe down and ran home as fast as his legs would carry him.

On the next day the second son set out, and the same thing happened. When he had been chopping for a while, the troll appeared again. The boy hardly dared look at him. He threw the axe down and ran home, just like his brother.

On the third day the Ash Lad wanted to go.

– You? said the two eldest. – Huh! You've never been outside the house!

The Ash Lad didn't say anything, just took some cheese with him.

When he had been chopping wood for a little while, the troll appeared and said:

– If you chop wood in my forest, I shall kill you!

The boy did not hesitate. He raced across to the cheese and squeezed it till the whey squirted out.

– If you don't shut up, he shouted to the troll, – I'll squeeze you the way I'm squeezing the water out of this white stone!

– No, dear fellow! Spare me! said the troll. – I'll help you cut some wood!

Well, on that condition the Ash Lad spared him. And as the troll was so good at chopping timber, they managed to fell and cut up many trees that day.

As dusk began to fall, the troll said:

– Now you can come with me. We are closer to my home than yours.

When they reached the troll's dwelling, he set about making the fire, while the boy was to fetch water for the porridge pot. But the two iron buckets were so big and heavy that he couldn't even budge them.

– There's no point using these thimbles. I'll fetch the whole well!

– No, my dear fellow, said the troll. – I can't afford to lose my well. You make the fire and I'll fetch the water.

Then they made a huge pot of porridge.

– If you agree, said the boy. – We could have an eating contest!

– Oh yes, replied the troll, as he was sure that he would win.

The Ash Lad managed to get his knapsack and tie it unseen across his stomach, and he shovelled more into the knapsack than he himself ate. When the knapsack was full, he took his knife and cut a slit in it. The troll looked at him, but didn't say a word.

When they had eaten a good while longer, the troll said:

– No! I can't possibly eat any more!

– But I'm barely half full! answered the boy. – If you do as I did and cut a hole in your stomach, then you can eat as much as you wish!

So the troll did as the boy said, and as you can imagine, that was the end of him. And the Ash Lad took all the silver and gold to be found in the mountain, and went home.

*(Norwegian folk tale)*

*If you are about to cross a stream*
*you should always spit, and say:*
*Troll in the depths,*
*See! the sign of the cross.*
*Keep away –*
*I am God's!*

*To defend yourself against the trolls
you must make the sign of the cross
or shout the name of Jesus.
It also helps to ring the church bells
three Thursday evenings in a row...*

A Forest Troll.

*Or if you dare:*
*You can tease the trolls*
*to such a fury*
*that they burst —*
*all on their own!*

But just as often the trolls fight among themselves.
When you hear the crash of thunder,
and see lightning rip the sky,
it is the giant mountain trolls
tumbling in a furious struggle
across the rugged peaks.
– I am the Master of Jotunheimen!
The reindeer flee in panic,
and the earth trembles!

*To see the world
through a troll's eye
is to discover
that everything wrong
seems right,
and everything right
seems wrong.*

*Beware,
and never try it!*

Christian Krohg: Theodor Kittelsen (1892)
Nasjonalgalleriet, Oslo.

Theodor Severin Kittelsen (1857 – 1914) is the Norwegian artist who, at the end of the last century, gave us the trolls – bursting out of the forests. We recognised them and felt that we had always known them, handed down as they were over the ages in our legends and folk tales.

Theodor Kittelsen was an unbelievably versatile artist. He was a story teller and satirist, poet and dreamer. And as master of our folk tales and lyrical portrayer of Nature he is unrivalled.

He was an accomplished writer, too, for example in his great works "Troldskab" (1892) and "Svartedauen" (1900).

After spending several years in Munich, Kittelsen began illustrating the folk tales in 1882. He collaborated felicitously with Erik Werenskiold, who had recommended him to the collector of folk tales, P. Chr. Asbjørnsen.
    Then came more stays abroad, in extreme poverty in Paris and Munich.

In the summer of 1887 he joined his sister and brother-in-law and moved to Skomvær Lighthouse, on the most outlying little skerry of the famous Lofoten Islands, the mighty mountain ridge which stretches out into the sea.

On this windswept little island, inaccessible in autumn and winter, he lived for two years. Here, far out in the Norwegian Sea, he experienced one of his most productive periods.

And here he created some of his masterpieces.
    Kittelsen's intense encounter with the violent forces of Nature, amid the wild and mysterious scenery of the North of Norway, gave birth to the Sea Troll and the Water Troll, the Mountain Troll and the Forest Troll… ("Troldskab").

# MY FATHER THEODOR KITTELSEN

**Theodor Kittelsen's youngest son, Helge Theodor Kittelsen, now 81 years old, shares some of his childhood memories with us:**

I was the youngest of nine brothers and sisters. When Father died in 1914, I was just four years old, but all the same I have several memories of him. In particular I remember his fine beard and kind eyes.

We children were convinced that Father had met trolls, water trolls and hulder nymphs, and it seemed quite natural to us that he was very upset one day when he heard that another artist was going to draw trolls:
– He? Sketch trolls? He has never seen a troll in his life!

Later, we felt insulted if others tried to portray trolls – it was just "copying", for they could have no idea what trolls looked like…

Father had a remarkable imagination, and the range of his artistic work was enormous. His painting "Strike" was the first social realist picture produced in Norway, but he was also a highly entertaining humorist and parodist. And his watercolours and folk tale illustrations have never been surpassed.

He was incredibly prolific, yet he never became rich. As a young man in Paris and Munich he had to go hungry at times, and some of his work took on an almost grotesque nature as a result. But after he had met my mother (which was in 1889), his pictures became lighter and gentler.

My mother Inga has frequently been called the first true artist's wife. With reason, I think. Father lived for his art, and spent the entire day in his studio. It was a holy place, no one trespassed there while he was working.

Father was not a practical man. He was shy, and totally dependent on Mother. He did not like being surrounded by strangers. Thus it was Mother who made the trips to town, conducted his business and sold his pictures. The family finances and the children's upbringing were her responsibilities.

One day the post office at Sigdal, two hours away by horse and sledge from our home "Lauvlia", would not cash her a money order which had arrived in Father's name. Father was furious, but did not lose his sense of humour and wrote out the following power of attorney in large, bold letters:

> I – Theodor Kittelsen – hereby authorise my wife Inga – née Dahl – to fetch and spend all my money.
>
> Th. Kittelsen

My parents were constantly short of money, but they managed to hide that truth from us. My eldest sister Ingrid told me that she was fifteen before she realised our parents had severe financial problems.

– May God preserve our children from becoming artists, Father used to say to Mother. And in a letter to a friend he wrote:

> "Many are the occasions on which it is burdensome to be an artist in Norway, so burdensome that it seems hopeless. But it is no use stopping at that point. One must pick oneself up, and continue. If I did not love Nature so, every flower and every stream, I do not think I would have the energy. Nature is wonderful solace."

After Father's death, Mother was in even greater financial straits. To keep herself and nine children alive, she had to sell Father's pictures. Most of them at ridiculously low prices. Some years later they were worth a fortune…

**In the autumn of 1990 the watercolour "The White Bear King Valemon" was sold at auction in Oslo for NOK 1.88 million, a record price for any single work by Kittelsen.**

The publishers would like to thank Mr. Helge Th. Kittelsen
for his willing cooperation and for permission
to reproduce photographs from his extensive picture
archive of his father's work.

Some of the originals of the illustrations in this book
are now in Nasjonalgalleriet, Oslo. They include works
from the series "Svartedauen", "Troldskab", and "Soria
Moria Slot".

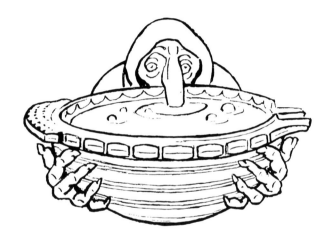

© MEDUSA A/S, 1991

N –1342 JAR, NORWAY

ISBN 82-90988-02-8

English translation: Joan Fuglesang

Printed by Nikolai Olsens Trykkeri a.s., Kolbotn, Norway